Disney

Winnie the Pooh

A FORGETFUL FRIEND

ADVANCE
PUBLISHERS

Advance Publishers, L.C.
1060 Maitland Center Commons, Suite 365
Maitland, FL 32751 USA

10 9 8 7 6 5 4 3 2 1
ISBN-10: 1-57973-396-4

One lovely spring morning, Pooh woke to the sweet smell of flowers drifting in through his window.

"Mmmmm," said Pooh as he stretched and yawned, "reminds me of honey!"

Pooh keeps his honey in pots made of clay.

CLAY

Clay is a special kind of soil. It's smooth and moist, and easy to shape into pottery. Once the pottery is baked in a hot oven, it hardens and can be used as vases, plates, and cups.

Of course, everything reminded Pooh of honey! Eating it was his favorite way to start the day . . . and end the day . . . and fill up the time in between!

Pooh wishes a little birdie would tell him where to find some honey!

BIRDS

A bird is an animal. Birds come in so many different colors! They can be blue, red, green, black, white, gray, yellow, or pink. Most birds fly, but some just swim or walk. Birds can sing, chirp, caw, or coo. Some birds can even talk!

Pooh went to his cupboard and pulled out a honeypot. "Oh, bother," he said, seeing that it was empty. He pulled out another . . . and another . . . but they were all empty, too!

It's a pleasure to be outside in warm, sunny spring weather.

SUN

Without the sun, there wouldn't be any life on the earth; our planet would be dark and frozen, and wouldn't have any plants or animals. Like all living things, we need the sun's light, heat, and energy to survive and grow.

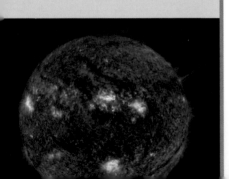

Pooh knew what he had to do: find more honey—the sooner, the better!

He stepped out into the sunshine. "Hmmm . . . which way should I go?" he asked himself.

That's when Pooh spotted a bee.

"Wait for me!" he called. But he soon lost sight of his guide.

Disappointed, he continued on his way. The soft, new grass tickled his feet. Pooh chuckled and looked down.

"Thank you, grass," he said. "I feel better now."

Grass is like a giant carpet for the outdoors!

GRASS

Grass grows in parks, gardens, and on backyards. But did you know that there are more than 10,000 kinds of grass? Cereals you eat such as oats, corn, and wheat are also grasses.

Soon Pooh came upon his friend Eeyore.

"Hello," said Pooh. "It's nice to see you."

"And it will be nice to see me again," replied Eeyore. "Don't forget, we're all meeting under the old oak tree at noon."

Thistles are prickly plants, but cactuses are even pricklier!

CACTUSES

Cactus plants, or cactuses, are covered with sharp spines. These spines keep desert animals from eating the plants, shade the plants, and collect dew.

Pooh didn't know what Eeyore was talking about.

"We are?" asked Pooh just as a thistle jabbed his bottom.

"It just goes to show you," said Eeyore. "Even the loveliest of days can turn thorny."

Eyore eats the whole thistle plant, including the leaves.

LEAVES

A leaf is part of a plant. Most plants have leaves, which grow out from their branches and stems. The leaf's job is to make food for the plant.

"I suppose," said Pooh. Then he waited, hoping Eeyore might say a little something more about why they were all getting together.

But Eeyore's mouth was full of thistles.

When Pooh saw Owl flying nearby, he decided to take a guess.

"It's a perfect day for gathering berries, isn't it?" Pooh asked.

"Yes," agreed Owl. "But, of course, we already have other plans."

OWLS

Owls cannot move their eyes from side to side the way people do. So, to see all around them, they turn their heads instead.

SEEDS

Most plants—from tall trees to tiny flowers—start off as seeds. Seeds grow in the soil. Seeds first sprout roots, which grow downward and anchor the seeds in the soil.

"Of course," said Pooh, who soon ran into Rabbit.

"It's perfect kite-flying weather, don't you think?" Pooh asked him.

"Uh-huh," Rabbit replied. "But obviously we won't have time today."

"Obviously," answered Pooh.

After Rabbit had gone, Pooh climbed up on the bridge.

"Think, think, think," he told himself as he looked at the down at the water.

"Pooh Sticks!" cried Pooh. "That's it! We must be meeting to play Pooh Sticks!"

Pooh Sticks go with the flow of the stream.

RIVERS AND STREAMS

Rivers are large, long bodies of flowing freshwater, and streams are small bodies of flowing freshwater.

Not all spring flowers grow from seeds.

DAFFODILS

If you plant daffodil bulbs in the fall, they'll bloom in the spring!

Pooh continued on his search for honey, imagining how much fun it was going to be to play his favorite game with his friends.

Bees don't sing—
but they do dance!

BEES
Bees do a special
dance that lets
other bees know
where the tasty
flowers are.

Finally, Pooh spotted the honey tree. A steady
buzzing filled the air all around it.
Pooh hoped what the bees were saying was,
"Come and get it!"

Honey isn't the only sweet treat you can find inside a tree.

SAP

Inside the trees is a liquid called sap. Sap helps bring water from the roots to the treetops. There are lots of maple trees in North America. People collect sap from maple trees and boil it to make maple syrup.

"Breakfast at last!" exclaimed Pooh as he climbed the tree. He gobbled up pawfuls of delicious golden honey, then scooped more into his pot.

When he was done, it was almost noon. Pooh went over to Piglet's house so that they could walk over to the old oak tree together.

Piglet loves baking with "haycorns."

ACORNS

Kerplunk! In the autumn you might be able to hear acorns drop to the ground. From tiny to tall . . . even the biggest, tallest oak trees begin as little acorn seeds.

"Hello, Pooh!" greeted Piglet. "I'll just pack the things we need and be back in a minute."

"I can't wait until it's my turn to toss everything into the stream," Pooh called from the doorstep.

Ducks waddle when they walk, but they're graceful when they swim.

DUCKS

Splish, splash! Ducks love the water. Can you see the duck's feet? Their feet are made for swimming. They are called webbed feet.

"Why would you toss food into the stream?" asked Piglet as they walked.

"Food?" Pooh replied. "I thought you were bringing Pooh Sticks."

"Pooh, don't you remember?" said Piglet. "We're having a picnic today—not playing Pooh Sticks."

"Oh!" Pooh exclaimed. "I forgot . . . and then I remembered . . . except I remembered what I thought I forgot instead of what I actually forgot . . . I think."

"No matter, buddy boy!" offered Tigger. "Let's eat!"

PINE TREES

This bristle cone pine is one of the oldest trees in the world. It is about 3,000 years old. The oldest tree in the world is called Methuselah. It grows in the United States. It is almost 5,000 years old!

Pooh settled down with his honeypot and dipped in a paw. It didn't matter that he had just had his breakfast a short while ago. Pooh's tummy was just as good at forgetting as Pooh was!

Spring gives birds lots of reasons to sing.

SPRING

These baby birds are hungry for worms. Their mommy finds lots of worms for them in the spring. The ground is soft now after being cold and hard all winter. Worms are easy to find, crawling around in the soil.

Later, the friends relaxed under the shade of the beautiful old oak.

"Do you know one of my favorite things about spring?" asked Rabbit. "Birds singing."

"And don't forget little bitty blossoms blossoming," Tigger added.

Sometimes Roo finds tiny insect friends in the grass.

LADYBUGS

Like most other insects, the ladybug has wings. But they are hidden! There are hard wing cases on top of a ladybug's real wings. Can you see this ladybug's wings?

"Or grass growing!" exclaimed Roo. So far that day he had rolled in it, and looked for insects in it, and lay on his back in it watching the clouds.

Bees don't just make honey, they make wax, too!

BEESWAX
People use beeswax to make candles, creams, furniture polish, lotions, and medicines.

By the time the picnic was over, Pooh's honeypot was nearly empty again.

"What a wonderful day," said Pooh with a happy sigh. "I won't ever forget it!"

"And if you do," said Piglet, "I promise to remind you."

He was a good friend that way.